Common Core

Standards for Mathematical Content

Domain Number and Operations in Base Ten

Cluster Work with numbers 11–19 to gain foundations for place value.

Standard K.NBT.1

Standards for Mathematical Practice

✔ Make sense of problems and persevere in solving them.

✔ Reason abstractly and quantitatively.

✔ Construct viable arguments and critique the reasoning of others.

✔ Model with mathematics.

✔ Use appropriate tools strategically.

✔ Attend to precision.

✔ Look for and make use of structure.

✔ Look for and express regularity in repeated reasoning.

Composing Numbers 11 to 19

Copyright © 2012 by Pearson Education, Inc., or its affiliates. All Rights Reserved. Printed in the United States of America. This publication is protected by copyright, and permission should be obtained from the publisher prior to any prohibited reproduction, storage in a retrieval system, or transmission in any form or by any means, electronic, mechanical, photocopying, recording, or likewise. For information regarding permissions, write to Rights Management & Contracts, Pearson Education, Inc., One Lake Street, Upper Saddle River, New Jersey 07458.

Pearson, Scott Foresman, Pearson Scott Foresman, and enVisionMATH are trademarks, in the U.S. and/or in other countries, of Pearson Education Inc., or its affiliates.

Common Core State Standards: © Copyright 2010. National Governors Association Center for Best Practices and Council of Chief State School Officers. All rights reserved.

UNDERSTANDING BY DESIGN® and UbD™ are trademarks of the Association for Supervision and Curriculum Development (ASCD), and are used under license.

ISBN-13: 978-0-328-67332-2
ISBN-10: 0-328-67332-3

6 7 8 9 10 V064 15 14 13 12

BIG IDEA **The Base-Ten Numeration System** The base ten numeration system is a scheme for recording numbers using digits 0-9, groups of ten, and place value.

ESSENTIAL UNDERSTANDINGS

10-1, 10-2, 10-3 Numbers from 11–19 can be represented as the sum of 10 and some more.

BIG IDEA **Practices, Processes, and Proficiencies** Mathematics content and practices can be applied to solve problems.

ESSENTIAL UNDERSTANDING

10-4 Patterns on the hundreds chart can be represented using number sentences and drawings.

Place Value

In our place value system, the position of a digit represents its value. In the number 15, for example, the 1 represents a group of 10, while the 5 stands for 5 ones. Place value is at the heart of our number system, and an understanding of place value concepts is essential when working with numbers in the years beyond kindergarten.

However, the place value system is not obvious to most children. The letter *m* stands for the sound /m/ regardless of where in a word it appears, and the color of a crayon remains the same regardless of whether it's in someone's hand, on a table, or in a box. Most young children therefore see no reason why the digit 2 should stand for twenty (two tens) when it is followed by another digit, but stand for 2 (two ones) when no other digit comes after it.

There will be time in the grades ahead for children to explore place value further and to develop a solid grasp of how it works. In kindergarten, place value instruction simply introduces children to the idea of grouping by tens and leftover ones. For children who are interested, it's fine to talk about how the first digit in 15 stands for a single ten. For most children, though, it's sufficient to have them compose and decompose teen numbers, using 10 as one of the addends, without worrying too much about why the numbers are written as they are.

Mathematical Practices: Use Structure

Be sure that children understand that 10 can be represented by 10 counters, or by a single filled ten frame, but that it cannot be represented by a single counter. Some children may try to represent 15 using 1 counter and 5 more counters, for example. Remind them that 15 is not 1 + 5, but rather 10 + 5. To help them, make certain that children are using the ten frames as much as possible to model teen numbers. Keep them grounded in the concrete as much as possible where place value concepts are concerned.

Composing and Decomposing Numbers

To understand teen numbers, children need to be able to think about a number such as 16 as the sum of two other numbers. That is, they need to be comfortable with composing and decomposing numbers. To *compose* numbers is to join two numbers to make a single number with the same value. To compose 12, for example, children can write the number sentence $10 + 2 = 12$. To *decompose* a number is to take it apart to make two numbers with the same total value. The number sentence $13 = 10 + 3$ shows one way to decompose 13.

For the numbers 11 through 19, which are studied in this topic, children are asked to compose and decompose using 10 as one of the addends. The boxes below show ways of composing or decomposing some of these numbers so 10 is one of the addends.

Compose:	Decompose:
$10 + 1 = 11$	$11 = 10 + 1$
$10 + 2 = 12$	$12 = 10 + 2$
$10 + 3 = 13$	$13 = 10 + 3$
$10 + 4 = 14$	$14 = 10 + 4$
$10 + 5 = 15$	$15 = 10 + 5$

Mathematical Practices: Reason Quantitatively

Encourage children to think in terms of ten and some more whenever possible. For example, when the class is lining up to go somewhere, consider having children form lines of ten with some left over. If there are 19 children in the class, for example, they can form a line of 10 and another line of 9 extras. Have them say the number sentence $10 + 9 = 19$ to go with the situation. You can also incorporate teen numbers into your daily routine. For example, each day during the initial meeting time you can provide the class with a sample of 11–19 ordinary classroom objects, such as markers, cubes, or pencils, and have children model counting them by making a group of ten with some left over.

For a complete list of *enVisionMATH* Professional Development resources in print, on DVD, and online, see the *Teacher's Program Overview*.

 INTERVENTION

ELL

Considerations for ELL Children

- In English, as with several other Western European languages, the number words for 11 and 12 do not follow the pattern of the number words for the numbers 13–19. Children with limited English skills may be tempted to call 11 "one-teen" and 12 "two-teen" by analogy with numbers such as fourteen, sixteen, and nineteen. Be sure children understand that the numbers are called "eleven" and "twelve." In particular, check that non-native speakers understand the words "eleven" and "twelve" when you are speaking them.

Special Needs

Considerations for Special Needs Children

- Using ten frames can be difficult for some special needs children. They may find it hard to manipulate the counters or to see them clearly. For these children, it may be helpful to provide larger ten frames. You can also have them work with a partner.

- The lessons in this topic require children to write individual numbers and number sentences. This may be difficult for children whose fine motor skills are weak or who struggle with handwriting. Instead of having these children write their answers, consider having them place small cards with numbers on them in the answer blanks instead. If you have inkpads and stamps with the numerals on them, you can have children use these as well.

Below Level

Considerations for Below-Level Children

Some children struggle with the concept that 10 individual objects can be combined to form a single group of 10. It can be helpful to work with these children to show that the quantities are actually the same.

- Model the connection between 10 ones and a group of ten as often as possible. For instance, scatter 10 counters on the floor or on a table and have children count them. Establish that there are 10 individual counters. Then scoop the counters into a small box. Point out that there are still 10 counters, but now they are all grouped together into 1 box: it is *1 group* of 10.

Advanced/Gifted

Considerations for Advanced/Gifted Children

Children who seem to quickly and easily understand teen numbers will benefit from activities such as the following:

- Ask children to compare teen numbers. For instance, ask children questions such as *Which is greater: 17 or 14?* as well as more complex questions such as *How much greater is 13 than 11?*

- Have children think about objects and body parts, such as fingers and toes, that typically come in groups of ten. Ask them to draw and label these objects and share their work with classmates.

Response to Intervention

 Ongoing Intervention
- Lessons with guiding questions to assess understanding
- Support to prevent misconceptions and to reteach

 Strategic Intervention
- Targeted to small groups who need more support
- Easy to implement

RTI **Intensive Intervention**
- Instruction to accelerate progress
- Instruction focused on foundational skills

MATHEMATICAL PRACTICES

Reading Comprehension and Problem Solving

Ⓒ **Use Structure:**

Using Reading Comprehension Strategies

Even when math problems are presented using a picture-book format, a good reading comprehension strategy to use in math problem solving is following directions.

Questions to Guide Comprehension

Use these questions with Lesson 10-4, Guided Practice. *What do you need to do first?* [Draw counters in the ten-frames.] *How many counters do you need to draw in the top ten-frame?* [9] *How do you know?* [Because the number 9 is written on the side] *What do you do next?* [Draw counters on the double ten-frame below.] *How many counters do you draw?* [19] *How do you know?* [Because the number 19 is written on the side] *What is the last thing you need to do?* [Write the number sentence to show how many.]

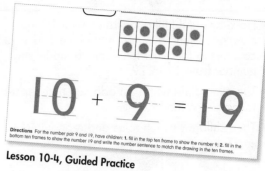

Lesson 10-4, Guided Practice

Act It Out! *How can you use counters and ten-frames to solve the problems on this page?* Have children fill ten-frames with the appropriate number of counters to show 9 and then 19. *How could we solve these problems by making groups of people?* Have 9 children stand in a row of 5 and another row of 4; have 19 children stand in a group of 10 and a group of 9 (5 children in one row and 4 in another).

Talk It Out! *How could you follow directions while you act out the problem?* Help children make up directions about filling in the ten-frames: *I need to put 9 counters in the top ten-frame. First I put a row of 5 counters at the top of the ten-frame. Then I put more counters on the second row and I count on from 5 until I get to 9: 6, 7, 8, 9.* Repeat for making 19. Then help children make up directions for writing the number sentence: *First, I write 10 to show that there is a full ten-frame. Then I check to see how many are in the second ten-frame. That's 9, so I write 9 in the second blank. The third blank gets the total number of counters. I know that has to be 19, because the problem asked me to draw 19. I'll write 19 in the last blank.*

Draw It Out! *How could you use crayons instead of counters to solve the problem?* Children can color the appropriate number of boxes in each ten-frame to make 9 or 19. They can count as they draw or use some other method of determining that they have the correct number.

Vocabulary Activities

How Many More X's?

Ⓒ **Attend to Precision** Explain that the questions *How many more?* and *How many in all?* sound alike, but they are not the same. Draw the picture at the right on the board.

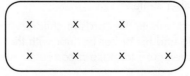

How many in all? 7 x's in all.

When I ask How many in all?, I want to know the total number of x's. I can count the x's and find that 3 x's and 4 more x's makes 7 x's in all. Draw a circle around the 7 x's. Tell children that when you say *How many in all?* they should draw a circle in the air to show that they need to find a total. Then draw the same picture elsewhere on the board and say, *When I ask How many more? I want to know how many x's to draw so that each row has the same number of x's.* Draw 1 more x in the top row to make equal groups. Tell children that when you say *How many more?* they should draw an x in the air to show that they need new objects to make two groups have the same number of objects.

How many more? 1 more x.

Writing Center

We've Been Framed!

Materials
(per pair) 10 red counters, 9 yellow counters, 2 ten-frames, writing paper

- Have one child fill a ten-frame with 10 red counters. Then have the child place 1 to 9 yellow counters in the other ten-frame to model any number from 11 to 19.
- The other child writes an addition number sentence to match the model.
- Then children switch roles and repeat the activity.

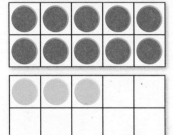

10 + 3 = 13

Building Center

Teetering Towers

Materials
(per child) 10 red connecting cubes, 9 blue connecting cubes, writing paper

- Have each child connect 10 red connecting cubes and balance the tower vertically. Have the child connect 1 blue cube to the top of the tower.
- Children then write an addition number sentence to match the cubes: 10 + 1 = 11.
- One at a time, have children carefully add 1 blue cube to their towers. After they add each cube, have children write the addition number sentence that matches the red and blue cubes.
- Allow children to rebalance each tower if it tips over. Have children continue until their towers are 19 cubes tall.

10 + 5 = 15

Movement Center

Find Your Partner

Materials
Index cards

- On pairs of index cards, write addition number sentences with a missing sum. Number sentences should show ways to make numbers 11 to 19, such as 10 + 1 = ___, 10 + 2 = ___, 10 + 3 = ___, etc. On separate index cards write the missing sum of each number sentence.
- Shuffle and distribute the cards to children. Instruct each child to find his or her partner with the matching index card to make a correct number sentence.
- Have children check each other's work. Collect, shuffle, and redistribute the index cards for additional practice.

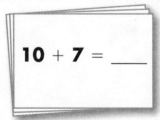

10 + 7 = ___

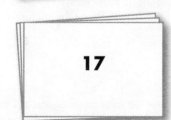

17

Art Center

Starry, Starry Night

Materials
Paper, crayons

- Each child chooses 2 crayons that are different colors.
- Have each child use the first crayon to draw 10 stars on the paper.
- Have each child use the second crayon to draw from 1 to 9 more stars.
- At the bottom of the paper, have each child write a number sentence to match the colors of the stars he or she drew. Remind children to carefully count each color of star before writing the number sentence.
- Display the pictures around the classroom.

Science Center

Green Teens

Materials
2 small rectangular boxes (such as shoeboxes), soil, plastic wrap, 18 bean seeds, index card, tape, water

- Line the inside bottom and sides of the boxes with plastic wrap. Then put soil into each box and trace the outline of a ten frame onto the topsoil of each box.
- Have children watch carefully as you place 10 bean seeds into the ten-frame soil of the first box and 8 bean seeds into the ten-frame soil of the second box. Add a little water to the soil.
- Invite volunteers to tell how many seeds are in each box and how many seeds there are in all. [10, 8, 18] Elicit that the matching addition number sentence is 10 + 8 = 18. Write the number sentence on an index card and tape it to the boxes.
- Display the boxes near sunlight. Add a little water to the soil every other day, and invite children to watch their bean sprouts grow.

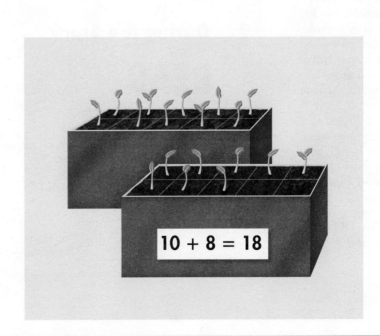

Whoo, Whoo! Time to Go!

This is a story in which children draw teen numbers on double ten-frames to express each number as the sum of a ten and some ones.

1 ▸ Before the Story

Picture Walk

Ask children to look at the pages. *What do you see in the pictures?* [Part of a train] *Have you ever ridden on a train? Would you like to ride on a train?* [Answers will vary.] *What kinds of noises do trains make?* [Possible answers: click-clack, whooo, chugga chugga choo]

Activate Prior Knowledge

In this story, we'll draw pictures that show different teen numbers. Let's practice drawing a picture of a teen number. Draw a double ten-frame on the board. Then write the number 11. *What number did I write?* [11] *Can I show 11 with just one ten-frame? Explain.* [No; there are only 10 spaces on a ten frame.] Touch the upper ten-frame. *Should I start by filling in this whole ten-frame, or just part of it?* [The whole frame] Have children help you draw in circles to fill the frame. Touch the lower ten-frame. *How many spaces do I need to fill in on this frame so there are 11 in all? Why?* [1 more, because 10 + 1 = 11] Say, *10 at the top and 1 more at the bottom shows 11,* and have children repeat after you. Repeat with 18 [10 and 8] and 13 [10 and 3].

This book belongs to:

Eva

Topic 10 Story

whoo, whoo! Time to Go!

There are 14 boxes.
We need 17 so we can go.
Whoo, whoo! Time to go?
No!

Topic 10 — 1

Ann brings one more box.
There are 15 boxes.
Whoo, whoo! Time to go?
No!

Topic 10 — 2

2 ▸ During the Story

READ

Read the story aloud for enjoyment. Then read each page aloud and wait for children to respond to the text. On each page, have children decide whether the train has enough boxes for it to go.

GESTURE

Have children hold up 10 fingers and then 4 more fingers to model the 14 boxes that are on the train to begin the story. Then turn to the next page. *Ann puts another box on the train. How many are there now? Show me with your fingers.* [15; a group of 10 and 5 more] Continue through the rest of the story.

b brings one
ore box.
here are 16 boxes.
hoo, whoo! Time
go?
o!

Topic 10 **3**

**Jan brings one
more box.
There are 17 boxes.
Whoo, whoo! Time
to go?
YES!!!**

Topic 10 **4**

Extension

Have children act out the story, using cubes for the boxes and a large toy truck or other object for the train. Have children revise the story so the train starts with 11 boxes and cannot go until there are 19 boxes on the train. Have children put 11 cubes in place and then gradually add cubes, saying the new number each time and writing it on the board.

You may wish to have children take home their Interactive Math Story and share what they have learned about modeling the numbers 11 to 19 on double ten-frames.

COLOR

Distribute the Interactive Math Story to children. Explain that they can color the outsides of the train cars any color they wish, but that they should not color the ten-frames where Ann and the other railroad workers put the boxes. Allow children to color the train cars on each page. Ask them to tell about one of their drawings, using the sentence frame: *I used [name of color] to color the train that had [number] boxes.*

WRITE

Have children read the number of boxes on the train given on each page. Then have them draw squares or circles on the train cars to show that number. Check that they are filling the top ten-frame on each train car and adding the appropriate number of extra counters on the lower ten-frame.

SPEAK

Ask children to retell the story in their own words. For each page, have volunteers explain how they knew how many spaces on the double ten-frame to fill. Have children tell what happens to the number of boxes as the story goes on. [It is 1 more each time.]

Name _____

DOMAIN Number and Operations in Base Ten

Topic 10

Composing Numbers 11 to 19

Review What You Know

1 ★★★★★★★★★★ **12**

2  **15**

3 6 ⑯ 19

4 ⑬ 14 18

Directions Have children: **1.** count the objects in the group and write how many; **2.** Count the objects in the group and write how many; **3.** circle the numeral 16; **4.** circle the numeral 13; **5.** draw 11 circles in the box.

© Pearson Education, Inc. K

Home-School Connection

Dear Family,
Today my class started Topic 10, **Composing Numbers 11 to 19.** I will learn ways to show these numbers as the sum of 10 and some extra ones. I will also learn to write number sentences to show these numbers in different ways. Here are some of the new math words I will be learning and some things we can do to help me with my math.

Love, _____

Book to Read

Reading math stories reinforces concepts. Look for this title in your local library:

What's New at the Zoo? by Suzanne Slade (Enslow Publishers, Inc., 2009)

Home Activity

Play "Ten and Some More." Hold up all 10 of your fingers. Ask your child to hold up the number of additional fingers needed to make 13 fingers in all. [3] Repeat with other numbers from 11 through 19.

My New Math Words

How many more?

How many more does the bottom row have?
The bottom row has 2 more.

How many more does the top row have?
The top row has 1 more.

Review What You Know

Purpose

Diagnose children's readiness by assessing prerequisite content. Assign each set of exercises and go over the answers with children.

Topic Essential Question

Children will be able to answer the Topic Essential Question by the end of the topic. Revisit the question throughout the topic. Then use the Topic 10 Performance Assessment.

• How can you add 1 ten and some ones to make the numbers 11 to 19?

How many more?

Cards can always be used as flash cards. Have children create large vocabulary cards with visuals to add to the classroom word wall.

Bumblebee Beehive

11 12 13 14 15 16 17 18 19 10

What You Need

1 two-color counter

10 tiles

Number of Players: 2 to 4

How to Play

1. Put a tile on each beehive.
2. Take turns. Flip the counter. If you get red, lose a turn.
3. If you get yellow, take a tile off one beehive. Say the number.
4. Play until no tiles are left on the hives.
5. The player with the most tiles wins.

Topic 10

one hundred ninety-two 192

Game

for school or home

Purpose

Provide children with an opportunity to practice prerequisite number skills. Before they begin the game, you may wish to have children count, starting from 1.

Math Project

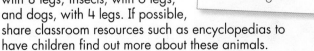

STEM Science

Show children a picture of a lobster. Tell children that a lobster is an ocean creature with a shell and 10 legs. Discuss other creatures that have more legs than we do—for example, spiders, with 8 legs, insects, with 6 legs, and dogs, with 4 legs. If possible, share classroom resources such as encyclopedias to have children find out more about these animals.

10 legs + 6 legs = 16 legs

Then have children draw a picture of a lobster, showing all 10 of its legs, and one other animal that was discussed. Have children write a number sentence on their picture to show how many legs in all.

Domain

Number and Operations in Base Ten

Cluster

Work with numbers 11–19 to gain foundations for place value.

Standard

K.NBT.1 Compose and decompose numbers from 11 to 19 into ten ones and some further ones, e.g., by using objects or drawings, and record each composition or decomposition by a drawing or equation (e.g., $18 = 10 + 8$); understand that these numbers are composed of ten ones and one, two, three, four, five, six, seven, eight, or nine ones.

Mathematical Practices

✔ Make sense of problems and persevere in solving them.

✔ Reason abstractly and quantitatively.

✔ Construct viable arguments and critique the reasoning of others.

✔ Model with mathematics.

✔ Use appropriate tools strategically.

✔ Attend to precision.

✔ Look for and make use of structure.

○ Look for and express regularity in repeated reasoning.

Making 11, 12, and 13

 **Lesson Overview**

Objective	Essential Understanding	Vocabulary	Materials
Children will represent 11, 12, and 13 as the composition of 10 plus 1, 2, or 3.	Numbers from 11–19 can be represented as the sum of 10 and some more.		Ten frame (or Teaching Tool 8), counters, paper bags

PROFESSIONAL DEVELOPMENT

Math Background

Composing teen numbers is fundamental to our decimal system. 11 should be thought of as 1 ten and 1 one, 12 as 1 ten and 2 ones, and 13 as 1 ten and 3 ones. Writing the numbers 11 through 19 as the sum of a ten and some ones is an important first step in understanding place value. It is also a prerequisite for fluency with addition strategies taught in first grade.

1 Daily Common Core Review

Daily Common Core Review

Name _____

Daily Common Core Review 10-1

⭐ Ⓐ △△△ △△ Ⓒ △△△△ △△△

Ⓑ △△△△ △△△ Ⓓ △△△△△ △△△△

❷ ☐☐☐☐
☐▨▨▨

Ⓐ $8 = 7 + 1$ Ⓒ $8 = 2 + 6$
Ⓑ $9 = 5 + 4$ Ⓓ $8 = 5 + 3$

Directions Have children mark the best answer. ⭐ Which picture shows 7 objects? ❷ Which number sentence describes the picture?

© 10-1

Copyright © Pearson Education, Inc., or its affiliates. All Rights Reserved.

Also available in print

Content Reviewed

Exercise 1   Making 7

Exercise 2   Writing Number Sentences for 8

 10–15 min # Problem-Based Interactive Learning

Hands-On Minds-On

Overview Children will write number sentences that represent the composition of 10 plus 1, 2, or 3 to make the numbers 11, 12, or 13.

Focus How can the parts of a number be represented as a number sentence?

Materials (per pair) Ten-frame (or Teaching Tool 8), 46 counters, 3 paper bags.

 *Engage*

Show ten-frame filled with counters. *How many counters are on this ten frame? How can you tell without counting?* [10; we have worked with this model many times.] *What if 1 more counter was added? How many would there be?* [11] *How do you know?* [11 is the next number after 10] *What if we added another counter?* [12] *Another counter after that?* [13]

Set the Purpose Remind children that they have been writing number sentences for numbers 10 and less. *Today, we will be counting more than 10 objects and learning how to write a number sentence that tells about how many.*

Connect Show the filled ten frame again. Write the number sentence 10 + ___ = ___ on the board. *The 10 at the beginning tells how many are shown on the ten frame. Are there any extra counters, or are there just 10?* [Just ten] Write 0 in the first blank. *The 0 shows that there are zero extra counters. We have 10 counters and zero extras. How many in all?* [10] Complete the number sentence: 10 + 0 = 10. *What does this number sentence mean?* [There are ten counters on the ten frame and zero extras, so there are 10 in all. 10 added to 0 equals 10.]

 MATHEMATICAL PRACTICES

Use Appropriate Tools Ask children how they could use a ten frame to model numbers 11 to 13.

Pose the Problem *Keith wants to write a number sentence to describe how many counters are in each bag. He also wants to use a ten frame so he can find out how many without counting. How can he write a number sentence that begins with 10 as one part?*

Small-Group Interaction Partners select one of the three bags and empty it on their workmat. They fill up the ten frame and then should notice that they have extras. Have them work on the number sentence that fits the number of counters in each bag. While children are working, ask: *What does the number 10 mean in this number sentence?* [How many counters on the ten frame] *Why is the number 10 the same color as the ten frame?* [They both represent 10, one using a number and the other using a drawing.] *What does the number after the plus sign represent?* [The number of extra counters; the number of counters more than 10] *What does the number after the equal sign mean?* [The total number of counters in the bag] Have children repeat with the other two bags.

Model and Share Ask pairs to model how they wrote number sentences to describe the content in their bags. *Describe the number 13.* [Ten and three more] *Which number is 10 and 2 more?* [12] *Describe the number 11.* [Ten and one more]

Use Drawings Ask children to select 11, 12, or 13 and make a drawing to represent the number using a ten frame as part of the drawing.

Lesson 10-1 Making 11, 12, and 13   Name _____

10 + ___ = ___   10 + ___ = ___   10 + ___ = ___

Answers will vary. Check children's work.

Topic 10 • Lesson 1   One Hundred ninety-three 193

 Extend

What would the number sentence 1 + 10 = 11 mean? How could it be represented as a drawing? [It would be one and one ten. It could be represented as a single counter and a ten frame.]

 DIGITAL   eTools **Counters** www.pearsonsuccessnet.com

Visual Learning

How many boxes?

Josh needs to know how many boxes of t-shirts have arrived for the school fair. How can he organize them so he can count them easily? [He can put them in sets of 10.]

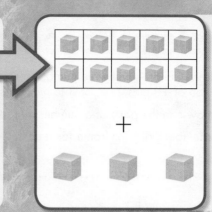

Josh put some of the boxes on the shelves in the picture. How many boxes fit on the shelves? How do you know? [10; the shelves look like a filled ten-frame, with 2 rows of 5.] *Are there any extra boxes that don't fit on the shelves? How many?* [Yes; 3]

1 Visual Learning

Set the Purpose Call children's attention to the Visual Learning Bridge at the top of the page. *In this lesson, you will learn how to show 11, 12, and 13 as the sum of ten and some extra.*

2 Guided Practice

Remind children that they will be writing number sentences using the plus and equal symbols.

Exercise 1
Error Intervention

If children switch the plus and equal signs and write a number sentence such as 10 = 2 + 12,

then remind them that the total number, in this case 12, must be by itself on one side of the equal sign.

Do you understand? *How can you write a number sentence to describe numbers that are 1, 2, or 3 more than 10?* [Write the number 10 and add on the extra 1, 2, or 3 to make 11, 12, or 13.]

Reteaching Have children work in pairs. Have one child hold up all ten fingers. The partner holds up one, two, or three fingers. Help children say the number sentence, touching the groups of fingers in turn.

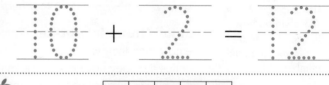

How many boxes?

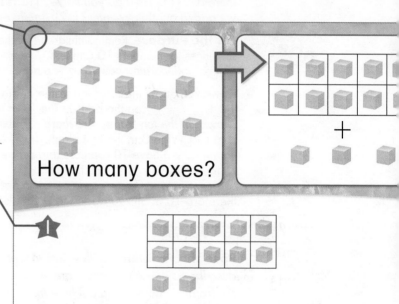

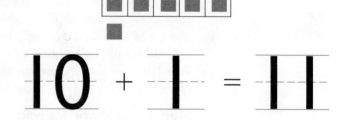

Directions Have children: **1.** trace the number sentence that matches the drawing; **2.** fill in the drawing to match the number sentence.

Topic 10 • Lesson 1

What does the 10 represent? [The number of boxes on the shelf; ten ones; one ten] *What does the 3 mean?* [The number of extra boxes after the ten-frame was filled; three; three ones]

10

3

$$10 + 3 = 13$$

13 boxes

What does the number sentence say? [Ten plus three is the same as 13; ten plus three equals thirteen.] *What does the = sign mean?* [The amount on one side is the same as the amount on the other.] *What is another way to say "thirteen?"* [One ten and 3 ones]

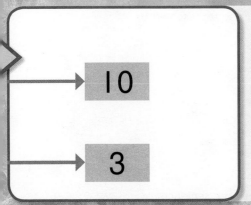

10

3

$$10 + 3 = 13$$

13 boxes

How Many?

 10 min

Materials: (per pair) 13 counters, ten-frame (or Teaching Tool 8)

• Divide children into pairs.

• Have one child choose 11, 12, or 13 counters. That child places 10 counters on the ten-frame and the extra counters beside the frame.

• The second child gives the number sentence that matches the picture, such as 10 + 2 = 12.

• Children switch roles and continue playing.

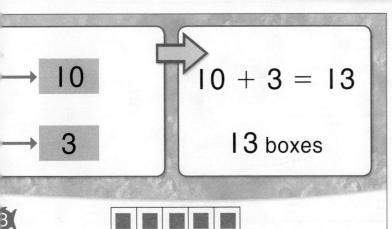

$$10 + 2 = 12$$

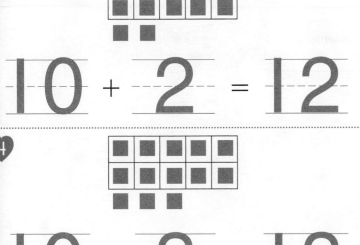

$$10 + 3 = 13$$

ections Have children: **3.** write the number sentence and fill in the drawing to show how to make 12; **4.** write the
number sentence and fill in the drawing to show how to make 13.

one hundred ninety-four **194**

3 **Independent Practice**

Remind children to fill the ten-frame and to draw extra counters on the side. Have them write a number sentence to show the total as the sum of one ten and some extra ones.

Close

Essential Understanding Numbers from 11–19 can be represented as the sum of 10 and some more.

 **ASSESSMENT**

Exercise 1 is worth 1 point.
Use the rubric to score Exercise 2.

Exercise 2

Reason Quantitatively Children should write the number sentence and fill in the drawing to show how to make 13.

ELL Model Thinking Aloud For children who need additional help with the assignment, say *First, I need to fill the ten frame with counters. Then I have to decide what to do with the extras.*

Student Samples
3-point answer The child writes the number sentence 10 + 3 = 13 and draws a full ten frame with three extra counters.

2-point answer The child writes the number sentence 10 + 3 = 13 but does not draw a picture that represents 10 and 3 more.

1-point answer The child does not write the number sentence 10 + 3 = 13.

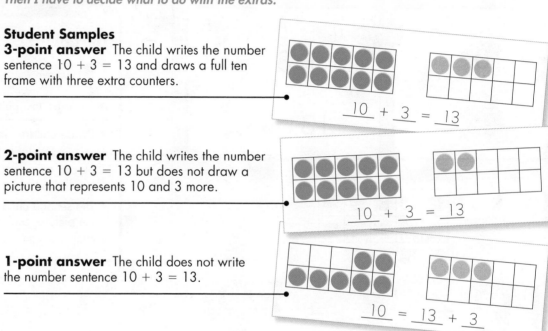

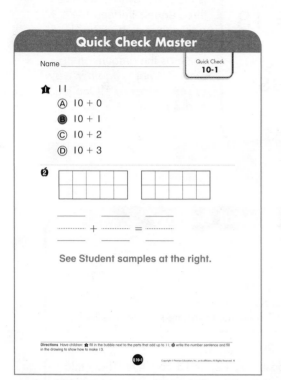

 **Formative** Assessment

Use the **Quick Check** to assess children's understanding.

Prescription for Differentiated Instruction
Use children's work on the **Quick Check** to prescribe differentiated instruction.

Points	Prescription
0–2	Intervention
3	On-Level
4	Advanced

Differentiated Instruction

Intervention

Making 11, 12, and 13

  10–15 min

Materials 13 counters, ten frame

- Have children place the ten-frame on a table and fill it with counters.
- Have them put down one more counter on the table. Now there are more than 10 counters on the table.
- Help children write the number sentence 10 + 1 = 11: a group of 10, plus one left over, is equal to 11.
- Repeat, filling the ten frame, putting down two and three counters on the table, and writing the corresponding number sentences.

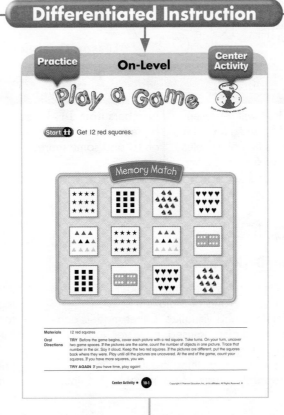

Practice | On-Level | Center Activity

Play a Game

Start ⬆⬆ Get 12 red squares.

Memory Match

Materials 12 red squares
Oral Directions TRY Before the game begins, cover each game space with a red square. Take turns. On your turn, uncover two game spaces. If the pictures are the same, count the number of objects in one picture. Trace that number in the air. Say it aloud. Keep the two red squares. If the pictures are different, put the squares back where they were. Play until all the pictures are uncovered. At the end of the game, count your squares. If you have more squares, you win.
TRY AGAIN If you have time, play again!

Center Activity ★ 10-1

Practice | Advanced | Center Activity

Play a Game

Start ⬆⬆ Get 12 red squares.

Memory Match

Materials 12 red squares
Oral Directions TRY Before the game begins, cover each game space with a red square. Take turns. On your turn, uncover two game spaces. If you see a picture and a number that shows how many objects are in that picture, explain why. Trace the number in the air. Say it aloud. Keep the two red squares. If you do not see a picture and a number that shows how many are in that picture, put the squares back where they were. Play until all the pictures are uncovered. At the end of the game, count your squares. If you have more squares, you win.
TRY AGAIN If you have time, play again!

Center Activity ★★ 10-1

ELL Partner Talk Listen for the words *eleven, twelve,* and *thirteen* when children are describing how many items are on each card.

Leveled Homework

Reteaching Master

Name
Making 11, 12, and 13
Reteaching 10-1

Directions Have children complete the drawings and number sentences to make 11 and then 13.

Practice Master

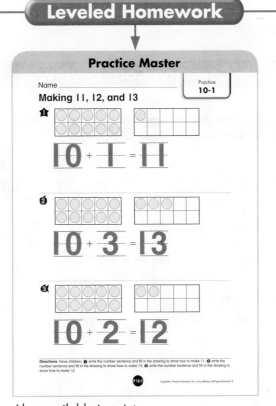

Name
Making 11, 12, and 13
Practice 10-1

Directions Have children: ★ write the number sentence and fill in the drawing to show how to make 11; ❷ write the number sentence and fill in the drawing to show how to make 13; ❸ write the number sentence and fill in the drawing to show how to make 12.

Enrichment Master

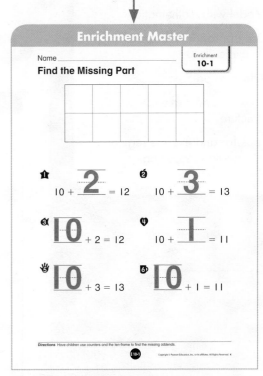

Name
Find the Missing Part
Enrichment 10-1

Directions Have children use counters and the ten-frame to find the missing addends.

Also available in print

Also available in print

Also available in print

DIGITAL eTools **Counters** www.pearsonsuccessnet.com

DIGITAL eTools **Counters** www.pearsonsuccessnet.com

DIGITAL eTools **Counters** www.pearsonsuccessnet.com

Domain

Number and Operations in Base Ten

Cluster

Work with numbers 11–19 to gain foundations for place value.

Standard

K.NBT.1 Compose and decompose numbers from 11 to 19 into ten ones and some further ones, e.g., by using objects or drawings, and record each composition or decomposition by a drawing or equation (e.g., $18 = 10 + 8$); understand that these numbers are composed of ten ones and one, two, three, four, five, six, seven, eight, or nine ones.

Mathematical Practices

✔ Make sense of problems and persevere in solving them.

✔ Reason abstractly and quantitatively.

◯ Construct viable arguments and critique the reasoning of others.

✔ Model with mathematics.

✔ Use appropriate tools strategically.

✔ Attend to precision.

✔ Look for and make use of structure.

◯ Look for and express regularity in repeated reasoning.

Making 14, 15, and 16

 **Lesson Overview**

Objective	Essential Understanding	Vocabulary	Materials
Children will represent 14, 15, and 16 as the composition of 10 plus 4, 5, or 6.	Numbers from 11–19 can be represented as the sum of 10 and some more.		Ten frames (or Teaching Tool 8), counters

 PROFESSIONAL DEVELOPMENT

Math Background

The ten-frame is a common model to represent 10. The two rows of 5 make it easy to understand and visualize. Other models can and should also be used, however, to help children begin to see ten ones as a single group of ten–something created by joining 10 separate things into a new whole. Other possible models are 10 snap cubes put together in a ten tower, 10 dots grouped to form a single unit of 10, or in a more abstract form, a long line that represents a ten strip or rod. To use these tools, children must understand how the model connects to written numerals.

1 Daily Common Core Review

Daily Common Core Review

Name _____

Daily Common Core Review **10-2**

❶ ☐☐☐☐☐
☐☐▨▨▨

Ⓐ $10 = 5 + 5$ Ⓒ $10 = 7 + 3$
$10 = 8 + 2$ $10 = 3 + 7$

Ⓑ $9 = 5 + 4$ Ⓓ $10 = 6 + 4$
$9 = 4 + 5$ $10 = 4 + 6$

❷ (ten frame with dots)

Ⓐ 13   Ⓒ 10
Ⓑ 12   Ⓓ 3

Directions Have children mark the best answer. ❶ Which number sentences describe the picture? ❷ How many counters are shown?

10-2

Also available in print

Content Reviewed

Exercise 1   Writing Number Sentences for 10
Exercise 2   Making 13

 10–15 min # Problem-Based Interactive Learning

Overview Children will write number sentences that represent the composition of 10 plus 4, 5, and 6 to make the numbers 14, 15, and 16.

Focus How can the parts of a number be represented as a number sentence?

Materials 2 ten-frames (or Teaching Tool 8), (per pair) 16 counters

 Engage

Set the Purpose Remind children that they have been writing number sentences for 11, 12, and 13. *Today, we will be learning how to write number sentences for 14, 15, and 16 when 10 is one of the parts.*

Connect Ask children to display 14 fingers. *Why is that impossible to do?* [People only have 10 fingers.] *Work with a partner and show me fourteen fingers using the fingers on both of your hands. Tell how many fingers you each used to make fourteen.* [Responses will vary.] Once children understand there are multiple ways to make 14, introduce the concept of counting on from 10. Count on from 10 to model the ease of counting when 10 is one part.

 MATHEMATICAL
PRACTICES

Use Appropriate Tools
Continue to stress the importance of the ten frame as an appropriate tool to think about numbers 14 to 16 as ten ones and some extra ones.

Pose the Problem *Chet and Devin are playing a game called "Make 15." Their goal is to fill the ten frames until they have placed 15 counters. Then they must write a number sentence to describe the picture they make for 15. How can they write a number sentence that begins with 10 as one part?*

Model *Let's play "Make 15." To play, partners take turns putting either 1 or 2 counters on the ten frame. As you play, fill up one row of the ten frame at a time. At the end of each turn, you must say how many counters are on the board. We'll play one game together.* Model the game with the displayed ten frames and counters. *To finish the game, we have to write a number sentence to describe what the ten frames look like. There are three number sentences on the page. Which number sentence should we use to show what your ten frames look like? Why?* [The sentence that shows = 15; the total is 15, not 14 or 16.] *What part of the total should we write in the first blank?* [10] *What part of the ten frames does that match?* [The filled ten frame at the top] *Do you need to count the counters to see if it is 10? Explain.* [No, if the ten frame is completely filled, it contains ten and it doesn't need to be counted.] *What number goes in the second blank?* [5] *What does 15 look like on ten frames?* [It is one complete ten frame plus one row of another ten frame.] Write the completed number sentence $10 + 5 = 15$ on the board and read it aloud with children.

Small-Group Interactions *Work with a partner and play three games: Make 14, Make 15, and Make 16. Write number sentences to describe each game.* Facilitate this process, listening to children as they place their counters on the ten frames and prompting them as they write their number sentences.

Lesson 10-2 Making 14, 15, and 16   Name _____

$$10 + 4 = 14$$
$$10 + 5 = 15$$
$$10 + 6 = 16$$

one hundred ninety-five 195

 Extend

Have pairs of children take turns counting on from 10 to 16.

DIGITAL eTools **Counters**
www.pearsonsuccessnet.com

Visual Learning

14 counters

Sondra has to write a number sentence to describe the number of counters. Why is she using two ten-frames? [She has more than 10 counters, so she needs to put the extras in another ten-frame.]

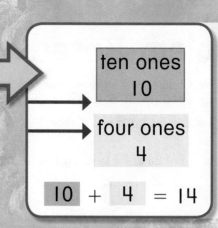

ten ones
10

four ones
4

10 + 4 = 14

The picture shows a number sentence. Read it with me. [Ten plus four equals fourteen.] *What does the 10 mean?* [Ten ones making a full ten-frame] *Why is the box with the 10 colored red?* [It tells about the red counters in the ten-frame on the top.] *Tell me what the number sentence means in your own words.* [Ten put together with 4 is the same as 14.]

---

1 Visual Learning

Set the Purpose Call children's attention to the **Visual Learning Bridge** at the top of the page. *In this lesson, you will learn how to show 14, 15, and 16 as the sum of ten and some extra ones.*

2 Guided Practice

Remind children that their first number sentence should begin with 10 to match the filled ten-frame.

Exercise 1
Error Intervention

If children write 14 as 41,

then tell them that the 1 needs to come first because it stands for the group of ten counters in the ten frame at the top of the picture.

Do you understand? *How can you write a number sentence to describe a teen number with 10 as one part?* [Fill a ten-frame and then add the number of counters you have left. Those parts (10 and the number of extras) go together to make the total number of counters. Write 10 + the number of extras = the total number of counters.]

Reteaching Have children write the number in each ten-frame to the right of the frame. For instance, in Example 1, children should write 10 to the right of the filled ten-frame and 4 to the right of the other frame. Then have children use these numbers to put together their number sentence.

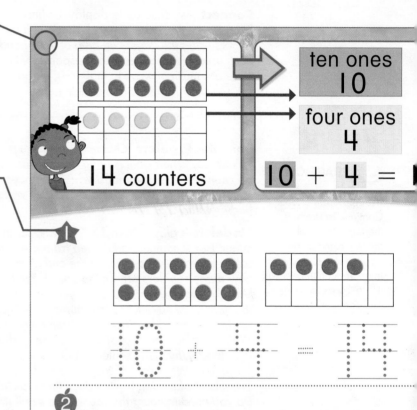

Directions Have children: **1.** trace the number sentence that matches the drawing; **2.** fill in the drawing to match the number sentence.

Topic 10 • Lesson 2

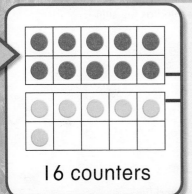

16 counters

Why did Sondra completely fill the first ten-frame? [She has more than 10 counters, so she starts by using 10 of them.] *Why didn't she fill the second ten-frame?* [She doesn't have enough counters; there were only 16 counters and if the first ten-frame is filled, just six are left.]

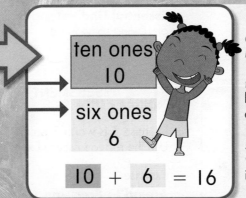

ten ones
10

six ones
6

10 + 6 = 16

This number sentence is different from the one in Box 2. How is it different? [It describes 16 instead of 14.] *How are the sentences alike?* [They both start with 10 to show that one of the parts is a group of 10.] *Tell me what the number sentence means in your own words.* [Ten put together with 6 is the same as 16.]

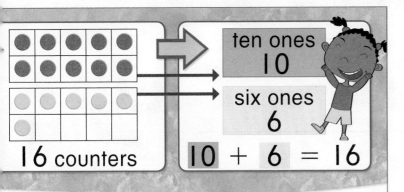

ten ones
10

six ones
6

16 counters

10 + 6 = 16

3

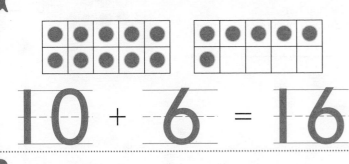

$$10 + 6 = 16$$

4

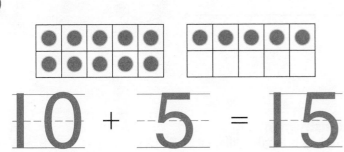

$$10 + 5 = 15$$

Directions Have children: **3.** write the number sentence and fill in the drawing to show how to make 16; **4.** write the number sentence and fill in the drawing to show how to make 15.

one hundred ninety-six **196**

Additional Activity

Number Sentence Match

🕐 10 min 👥

Materials (per pair) 6 index cards, each with a number sentence 10 + 1 = 11 up through 10 + 6 = 16; 6 index cards, each with a drawing showing 11 through 16 (a filled ten-frame and 1 through 6 extras in a second ten-frame)

- Divide children into pairs.
- Children mix the cards and place them facedown in a 3 × 4 grid.
- Children take turns flipping over two cards. If the cards match (such as 10 + 2 = 12 and the drawing of 12 counters), the child keeps the cards. Otherwise, the cards are turned over and placed in their original positions.
- Keep playing until all the cards are gone. The winner is the player with the most cards.

---

3 **Independent Practice**

Have children check to make sure their drawing matches their number sentence.

196A

Close

Essential Understanding Numbers from 11–19 can be represented as the sum of 10 and some more.

 ASSESSMENT

Exercise 1 is worth 1 point.
Use the rubric to score Exercise 2.

Exercise 2

Attend to Precision Children should write the number sentence and fill in the drawing to show how to make 16.

ELL **Model Thinking Aloud** For children who need additional help understanding what to do, say *I need to do two things. First, I need to draw a picture that shows 16. Then, I need to write a number sentence that tells about what I did.*

Student Samples
3-point answer The child writes the number sentence $10 + 6 = 16$ and draws a picture showing 10 counters in the first ten-frame and six in the second.

2-point answer The child writes the number sentence $10 + 6 = 16$ but does not draw a picture that shows 10 and 6 more.

1-point answer The child does not write the number sentence $10 + 6 = 16$.

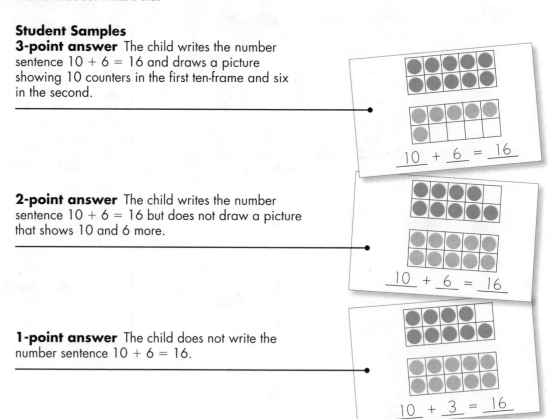

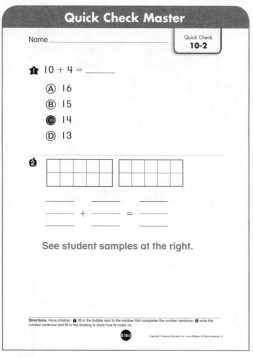

Formative Assessment

Use the **Quick Check** to assess children's understanding.

Prescription for Differentiated Instruction
Use children's work on the **Quick Check** to prescribe differentiated instruction.

Points	Prescription
0–2	**Intervention**
3	**On-Level**
4	**Advanced**

Differentiated Instruction

Intervention

Making 14, 15, and 16

🕐 10–15 min 👥

Materials 16 counters, 2 ten-frames for display, number cube

- Have children help you fill one of the ten frames with counters.

- Put the number cube down so 4 is showing. Have children put 4 counters down on the second ten frame to show that number.

- Ask children how many counters are in the filled ten frame. [10] Repeat for the second frame [4]. Touch the filled ten frame and say 10. Touch the other ten frame and say + 4. Touch both ten frames and say 14. Have children say the number sentence with you.

- Repeat, with the numbers 15 and 16 as needed.

Practice | **On-Level** | **Center Activity**

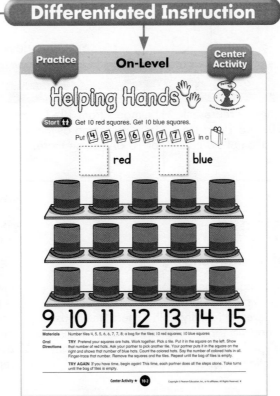

Helping Hands 🖐️

Start 👫 Get 10 red squares. Get 10 blue squares.

Put 4 5 5 6 6 7 7 8 in a 📖.

☐ red   ☐ blue

9 10 11 12 13 14 15

Materials: Number tiles 4, 5, 5, 6, 6, 7, 7, 8; a bag for the tiles; 10 red squares; 10 blue squares

Oral Directions: **TRY** Pretend your squares are hats. Work together. Pick a tile. Put it in the square on the left. Show that number of red hats. Ask your partner to pick another tile. Your partner puts it in the square on the right and shows that number of blue hats. Count the colored hats in all. Say the number of colored hats in all. Finger-trace that number. Remove the squares and the tiles. Repeat until the bag of tiles is empty.

TRY AGAIN If you have time, begin again! This time, each partner does all the steps alone. Take turns until the bag of tiles is empty.

Center Activity ★ 10-2

Practice | **Advanced** | **Center Activity**

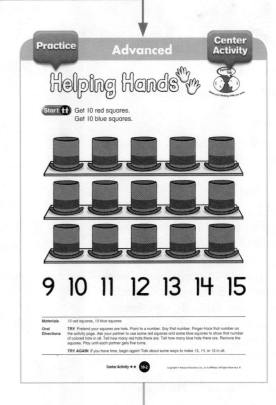

Helping Hands 🖐️

Start 👫 Get 10 red squares. Get 10 blue squares.

9 10 11 12 13 14 15

Materials: 10 red squares, 10 blue squares

Oral Directions: **TRY** Pretend your squares are hats. Point to a number. Say that number. Finger-trace that number on the activity page. Ask your partner to use some red squares and some blue squares to show that number of colored hats in all. Tell how many red hats there are. Tell how many blue hats there are. Remove the squares. Play until each partner gets five turns.

TRY AGAIN If you have time, begin again! Talk about some ways to make 13, 14, or 15 in all.

Center Activity ★★ 10-2

ELL Partner Talk Listen for the words *fourteen*, *fifteen*, and *sixteen* when children are describing how many hats there are in all.

Leveled Homework

Reteaching Master

Name _____ | Reteaching 10-2

Making 14, 15, and 16

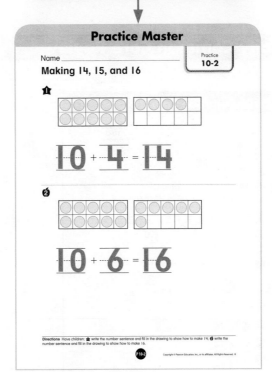

10   4   14 in all

10 + 4 = 14

❶

10   6   16 in all

10 + 6 = 16

Directions: Have children tell how many are in each ten-frame, then tell how many in all, and finally write the number sentence that goes with the picture.

Practice Master

Name _____ | Practice 10-2

Making 14, 15, and 16

❶

10 + 4 = 14

❷

10 + 6 = 16

Directions: Have children: ❶ write the number sentence and fill in the drawing to show how to make 14; ❷ write the number sentence and fill in the drawing to show how to make 16.

Enrichment Master

Name _____ | Enrichment 10-2

Circle Ten

❶

10 + 5 = 15

❷

10 + 6 = 16

❸

10 + 4 = 14

Directions: Have children circle a group of 10 counters and write a number sentence to show how to make 14, 15, or 16.

Also available in print | Also available in print | Also available in print

 eTools **Counters** www.pearsonsuccessnet.com

 eTools **Counters** www.pearsonsuccessnet.com

eTools **Counters** www.pearsonsuccessnet.com

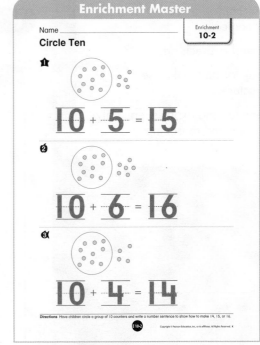

Domain

Number and Operations in Base Ten

Cluster

Work with numbers 11–19 to gain foundations for place value.

Standard

K.NBT.1 Compose and decompose numbers from 11 to 19 into ten ones and some further ones, e.g., by using objects or drawings, and record each composition or decomposition by a drawing or equation (e.g., $18 = 10 + 8$); understand that these numbers are composed of ten ones and one, two, three, four, five, six, seven, eight, or nine ones.

Mathematical Practices

✔ Make sense of problems and persevere in solving them.

✔ Reason abstractly and quantitatively.

○ Construct viable arguments and critique the reasoning of others.

✔ Model with mathematics.

✔ Use appropriate tools strategically.

✔ Attend to precision.

○ Look for and make use of structure.

✔ Look for and express regularity in repeated reasoning.

Making 17, 18, and 19

 **Lesson Overview**

Objective	Essential Understanding	Vocabulary	Materials
Children will represent 17, 18, and 19 as the composition of 10 plus 7, 8, or 9.	Numbers from 11–19 can be represented as the sum of 10 and some more.	How many more?	2 ten frames (or Teaching Tool 8), counters

 PROFESSIONAL DEVELOPMENT

Math Background

Composing numbers when ten is one of the addends provides an excellent opportunity for children to identify both general methods and shortcuts for calculations. "How many more" problems represent a type of addition/subtraction situation in which one part and the whole are known and the other part is missing. If children can see this type of problem visually with drawings and write number sentences that describe them, they can begin to see the regularity in mathematics and repeat their reasoning.

1 Daily Common Core Review

Daily Common Core Review

Name _____

Daily Common
Core Review
10-3

⭐ $10 + 5 = $ _____

Ⓐ 10   Ⓒ 16

Ⓑ 15   Ⓓ 51

2

Ⓐ 9, 10, 4, 5, 6, 7, 1, 2, 3, 8

Ⓑ 1, 3, 2, 4, 5, 6, 8, 7, 9, 10

Ⓒ 1, 2, 9, 8, 7, 6, 5, 4, 3, 10

Ⓓ 1, 2, 3, 4, 5, 6, 7, 8, 9, 10

3

Directions Have children mark the best answer. ⭐ Which number completes the number sentence? ❷ Which shows the numbers in order? ❸ Which group shows 2 fewer?

Ⓒ Copyright © Pearson Education, Inc., or its affiliates. All Rights Reserved. K

Content Reviewed

Exercise 1   Making 15

Exercise 2   Ordering Numbers Through 10

Exercise 3   Identify 2 Fewer

Also available in print

 10–15 min **Problem-Based Interactive Learning**

Overview Children will write number sentences that represent the composition of 10 plus 7, 8, and 9 to make the numbers 17, 18, and 19.

Focus How can the parts of a number be represented as a drawing or as a number sentence with 10 as one of the parts?

Materials 2 ten frames (or Teaching Tool 8), (per pair) 10 counters

Vocabulary How many more?

Set the Purpose Remind children that they have been making teen numbers by putting together 10 and some ones, and that they have been describing the numbers using drawings and number sentences. *Today, we will be describing the last of the teen numbers.*

Connect Draw a group of 10 counters on the board. Count them with children. Then draw a second group of 6 counters. Establish that there are 16 in all. *We counted 14, 15, 16. What if I drew another counter? How many would there be? Count with me...14, 15, 16...* Elicit that the next number is 17. Draw a seventeenth counter. *How many groups of ten do you need to show 17?* [1 group of ten] *How many extra ones are there?* [7]

MATHEMATICAL
PRACTICES

Repeated Reasoning
Point out that children can count on from 10 to solve the question *How many more?* or they can count how many counters are needed on the second ten frame to make the total. Emphasize that either way, the answer is the same.

Pose the Problem *Lance has already made 10 candy apples for the school carnival. How many more does he need to make to have 18 for his carnival booth? How can you use the ten-frames to write a number sentence that shows the problem?*

Academic Vocabulary Show a completed ten frame. *How many counters do you see?* [10] *I want to show 16. I have to add some more counters on another ten frame. How many more counters do I have to add so I have 16?* [6] Model putting down 6 more counters on the second ten frame. *I had ten. When I put down 6 more counters, it makes 16.* Empty the second ten frame. *I have 10 counters. I want to show 17. How many more counters do I need to add so I have 17 counters total?* [7] Model putting down 7 more counters. *I had 10. I added 7 more. Now I have 17. There are 7 counters more than 10 to make 17 counters all together.* Continue the same process for 18 and 19 counters.

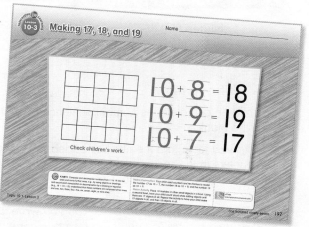

Model Restate Lance's problem. Refer children to the workmat and ask them to use their counters to show 18 on their mats. *How many apples did Lance have already for the school carnival?* [10] *Which ten frame shows ten?* [The filled one on top] *He needed 18 apples in all. How many more did he need to make to have 18 apples?* [8] *Which ten frame shows 8 apples?* [The bottom one] *Does Lance have all the apples he needs now?* [Yes] Write 10 + 8 = 18 and ask children to record the number sentence on their workmat.

Small-Group Interactions *Work with a partner. Solve two new problems, one for 19 apples and one for 17 apples. Write a number sentence for each problem.* Emphasize the need to find the addends rather than the sum when writing the number sentence.

Suppose Lance already had 10 candy apples, but he needed to have 20 for his booth. How could you use a number sentence and a drawing to find how many more apples he would need to make? [To make 20, you need 2 complete ten frames; Lance has already made 10, so he has enough to fill one frame; to make 20, you need to fill the other frame, so he needs to make 10 more candy apples.]

eTools **Counters**
www.pearsonsuccessnet.com

Visual Learning

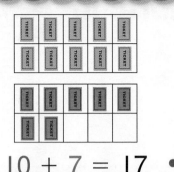

$10 + 7 = 17$

Samantha ordered 17 tickets for a carnival. She already had 10 tickets. How could she find out how many more tickets she needs? [She could think of a 10 on one ten frame and then show 7 on the other ten frame.]

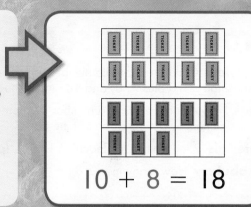

$10 + 8 = 18$

Now Samantha needs 18 tickets. She still has one set of 10. How many more tickets does she need? [8] *How do you know?* [There are 8 counters in the second ten frame. When that is put together with 10, you get 18.]

1 Visual Learning

Set the Purpose Call children's attention to the Visual Learning Bridge at the top of the page. *In this lesson, you will learn how many more you need to add to 10 to make 17, 18, and 19.*

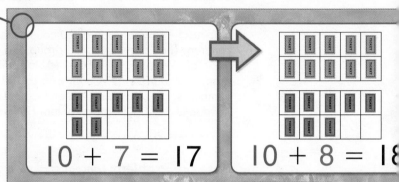

$10 + 7 = 17$ $10 + 8 = 18$

2 Guided Practice

Remind children that they need to find "how many more," not "how many in all."

Exercise 1
Error Intervention

If children complete the number sentence by writing 17 rather than 7 in the blank,

then show them that the number added to ten must be the number of counters in the second ten frame, and point out that the total is already written in the number sentence.

Do you understand? *How can you write a number sentence and draw a picture to describe a teen number with ten as one part?* [Fill one ten frame with counters to show 10. Add counters to the other ten frame until the total number of counters equals the teen number. The number of counters in each ten frame shows the teen number as ten and some more.]

Reteaching Help children make 18 on a pair of ten frames. Touch the filled ten frame and say *10.* Touch the second ten frame and say *plus something.* Indicate both frames together and say *equals 18.* Repeat, having children say the words with you. Then have children count how many spaces are filled on the second ten frame to find the missing amount. Repeat with 17 and 19 as needed.

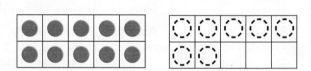

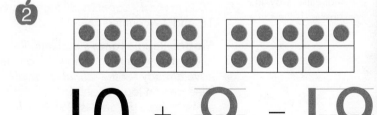

$10 + 7 = 17$

$10 + 9 = 19$

Directions Have children: **1.** show how many more counters would make 17 by filling in the missing part of the drawing and writing the missing number in the number sentence; **2.** fill in the missing numbers in the number sentence to match the picture.

Topic 10 • Lesson 3

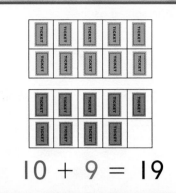

$$10 + 9 = 19$$

Tell a story about this drawing. Begin "Samantha has 10 tickets." Use the words "How many more?" [Answers will vary but should fit the number sentence 10 + 9 = 19.]

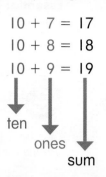

$$10 + 7 = 17$$
$$10 + 8 = 18$$
$$10 + 9 = 19$$

ten

ones

sum

How are these number sentences alike? [They all begin with 10 and then have some ones added.] *What does the word "sum" mean?* [The total number of items all together.]

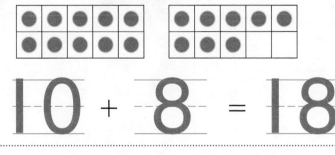

$$0 + 9 = 19$$

$$10 + 7 = 17$$
$$10 + 8 = 18$$
$$10 + 9 = 19$$

ten

ones

sum

3

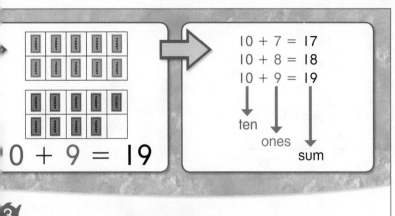

$$10 + 8 = 18$$

4

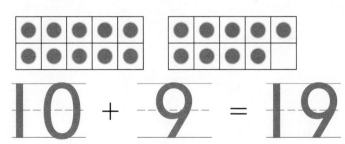

$$10 + 9 = 19$$

rections Have children: **3.** write the number sentence and fill in the drawing to show how to make 18; **4.** write the mber sentence and fill in the drawing to show how to make 19.

one hundred ninety-eight   **198**

Additional Activity

Stick Tallies

 10 min

Materials Craft sticks, large paper, glue or paste

- Children choose to represent either 17, 18, or 19. They count out that many sticks.

- They arrange the sticks in three groups of 5 and some left over, as in the picture below. Have them glue the sticks in place once you have checked that the arrangement and total number are correct.

- When they have made two groups of 5 (which makes a group of 10), they draw a circle around it.

- Finally, they write the number sentence that matches the picture; in this case, 10 + 8 = 18.

3 **Independent Practice**

Have children check to make sure their number sentences and drawings refer to the same numbers.

Close

Essential Understanding Numbers from 11–19 can be represented as the sum of 10 and some more.

 **ASSESSMENT**

Exercise 1 is worth 1 point.
Use the rubric to score Exercise 2.

Exercise 2

Reason Quantitatively Children should write the number sentence and fill in the drawing to show how to make 18.

ELL Model Thinking Aloud For children who need additional help understanding what to do, say *I already know the total: it's 18. I need to know how to draw 18 in the ten frames. I need to know what parts of 18 to show.*

Student Samples
3-point answer The child writes the number sentence 10 + 8 = 18 and draws a picture showing 10 counters in the first ten frame and 8 in the second.

2-point answer The child writes the number sentence 10 + 8 = 18 but does not draw a picture that shows 10 and 8 more.

1-point answer The child does not write the number sentence 10 + 8 = 18.

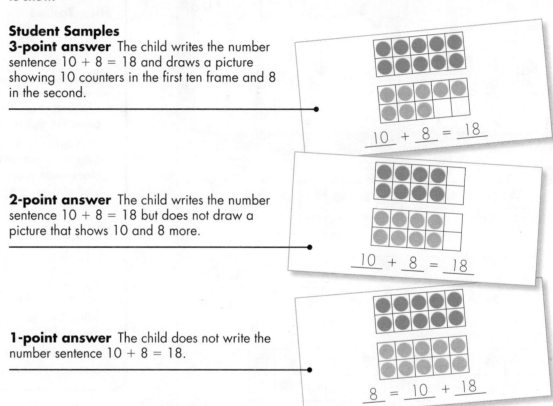

Quick Check Master

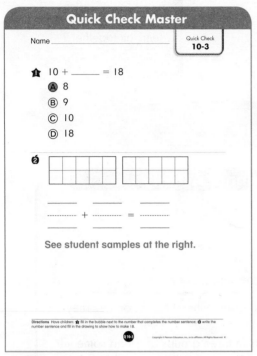

Formative Assessment

Use the **Quick Check** to assess children's understanding.

Prescription for Differentiated Instruction
Use children's work on the **Quick Check** to prescribe differentiated instruction.

Points	Prescription
0–2	Intervention
3	On-Level
4	Advanced

Differentiated Instruction

Intervention

Making 17, 18, and 19

 10–15 min

Materials 20 counters, 2 ten frames for display

- Have children help you fill one of the ten frames with counters.
- Take a handful of the remaining counters. Show them to children. Ask children to estimate how many there are.
- Help children put the counters on the second ten frame.
- Touch the filled ten frame and say "10." Touch the other ten frame and say the number of counters. Have children repeat. Then help children identify how many counters there are in all.
- Repeat, taking a different number of counters. Continue with other amounts as needed.

Practice | **On-Level** | **Center Activity**

Practice | **Advanced** | **Center Activity**

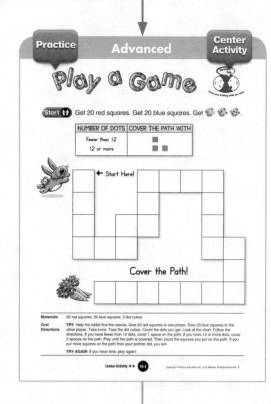

Leveled Homework

Reteaching Master

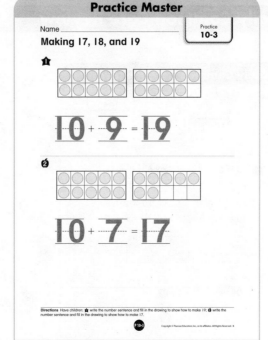

Also available in print

Practice Master

Name _____
Making 17, 18, and 19   Practice 10-3

Also available in print

Enrichment Master

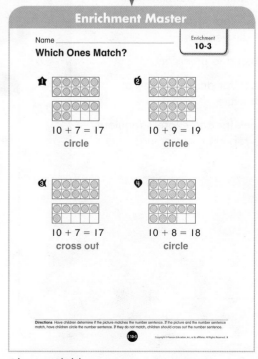

Also available in print

DIGITAL | eTools **Counters**
www.pearsonsuccessnet.com

DIGITAL | eTools **Counters**
www.pearsonsuccessnet.com

DIGITAL | eTools **Counters**
www.pearsonsuccessnet.com

Domain
Number and Operations in Base Ten

Cluster
Work with numbers 11–19 to gain foundations for place value.

Standard
K.NBT.1 Compose and decompose numbers from 11 to 19 into ten ones and some further ones, e.g., by using objects or drawings, and record each composition or decomposition by a drawing or equation (e.g., $18 = 10 + 8$); understand that these numbers are composed of ten ones and one, two, three, four, five, six, seven, eight, or nine ones.

Mathematical Practices

☑ Make sense of problems and persevere in solving them.

☑ Reason abstractly and quantitatively.

○ Construct viable arguments and critique the reasoning of others.

☑ Model with mathematics.

☑ Use appropriate tools strategically.

☑ Attend to precision.

☑ Look for and make use of structure.

☑ Look for and express regularity in repeated reasoning.

Problem Solving: Look for a Pattern

 **Lesson Overview**

Objective	Essential Understanding	Vocabulary	Materials
Children will use drawings and number sentences to identify patterns on the first two rows of the hundreds chart.	Patterns on the hundreds chart can be represented using number sentences and drawings.		Large sheet of chart paper, glue or tape, markers, 2 sets of number card pairs; (per pair) 3 ten-frames (or Teaching Tool 8), 30 counters

© **PROFESSIONAL DEVELOPMENT**

Math Background

The pattern on the 100s chart is part of a counting pattern that emphasizes place value. Because each row has ten numbers, each number in each row is 10 more or 10 less than the number directly above or below it. Recognizing these patterns is an important part of recognizing structure in mathematics.

In particular, the structure of our decimal system allows us to generate computation shortcuts and procedures. While young children will not understand the benefit of this structure at this level, the patterns on the first two rows of the 100s chart can provide a beginning foundation for understanding place value.

1 Daily Common Core Review

Daily Common Core Review

Name _____

Daily Common Core Review 10-4

⭐

Ⓐ $10 = 6 + 4$ Ⓒ $6 = 4 + 2$
$10 = 4 + 6$ $6 = 3 + 3$

Ⓑ $10 = 7 + 3$ Ⓓ $10 = 2 + 8$
$10 = 5 + 5$ $10 = 8 + 2$

❷

Ⓐ 9   Ⓒ 15
Ⓑ 10   Ⓓ 19

Directions Have children mark the best answer. ⭐ Which number sentences describe the picture? ❷ How many counters are shown?

10-4

Copyright © Pearson Education, Inc., or its affiliates. All Rights Reserved. K

Content Reviewed
Exercise 1   Writing Number Sentences for 10
Exercise 2   Making 17, 18, and 19

Also available in print

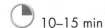

 10–15 min ## Problem-Based Interactive Learning

Overview Children will identify patterns on the first two rows of the hundred chart using drawings and number sentences to represent the numbers.

Focus What patterns are there on the first two rows of the hundred chart, and how can the patterns be represented?

Materials Large piece of butcher or chart paper that shows the first two rows of the hundred chart with extra space beneath the bottom row of numbers; glue or tape; markers; 2 sets of number card pairs (1 and 11, 2 and 12, 3 and 13, and so on to 10 and 20); (per pair) 3 ten-frames (or Teaching Tool 8), 30 counters

Set the Purpose Display a 100s chart and confirm children recognize it. *We have used a 100s chart to count to 100 and to look for counting patterns. Today, we will be looking very carefully at just the first two rows of the hundred chart and looking for more patterns.*

Connect *Let's look at the first two rows of the hundred chart.* Show the chart paper with the first two rows labeled with numbers. *What patterns do you see?* [Responses will vary; focus on the ones that involve number concepts.]

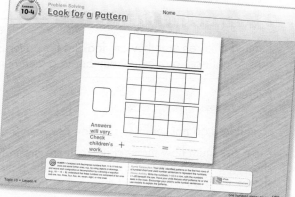

Pose the Problem *How can we represent the patterns we find in the first two rows of the 100s chart?*

Model *Let's do one together.* Draw 6 and 16 from the pile of number cards. *How could we show these two numbers with counters on the ten-frames?* [Put the counters on the ten frame for the top number and use both ten frames for the bottom number.] Have children set the counters on their workmats. *Do the two arrangements look the same or different? How?* [6 needs just one ten frame, but 16 needs two; the frame for 6 matches the bottom ten frame for 16.] *What goes with 6 to make 16?* [10] *How can we write a number sentence that shows this relationship?* [10 + 6 = 16]

Think, Pair, and Share Give each pair of children a pair of number cards. Ask children to use their counters to represent their numbers on their workmat. Have them write the number sentence they used. If their representations are correct, have them use the paper ten-frames to make a copy of their workmat and attach it to the chart in the appropriate space under their number.

Small-Group Interactions *Look at the chart. What patterns can you see?* [Again, the responses will vary.] Select one number in the top row. *What happens when you move straight down to the second row?* [The number gets bigger than the one on top; it has a 1 in front of the number; it has an extra ten frame that is entirely filled.] *How does the number sentence help you see the pattern?* [10 is added to the number on the top.] *Does the same thing happen in the other columns?* [Yes] Show children that the pattern of inserting 1 in front of the original number doesn't work for the number pair 10 and 20.

MATHEMATICAL PRACTICES

Use Structure
Use colors or labels to highlight the "ten more" pattern on the 100s chart. Children can learn to look closely for patterns in the structure of numbers. The hundred chart, with its rows of 10, is a valuable tool to help children see the patterns in place value.

Start with a number on the second row. Go straight up to a new number. What pattern do you see? [10 is subtracted from the number; the number is ten less than the number you started with.]

 **eTools Counters** www.pearsonsuccessnet.com

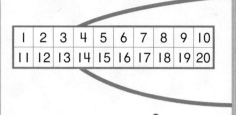

Visual Learning

Read and Understand

1	2	3	4	5	6	7	8	9	10
11	12	13	14	15	16	17	18	19	20

What patterns do you see in the top two rows on the hundred chart? [Possible responses: the numbers on the bottom are bigger; the digits on the right in each column are the same.]

Plan

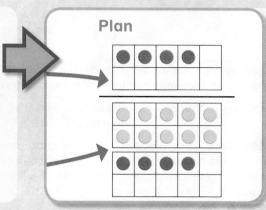

Look at the two picture How are the drawings alike? [Both have a ten-frame with four counters.] *How are they different?* [The drawing for 14 has one completed ten-frame and the drawing for 4 does not.]

1 Visual Learning

Set the Purpose Call children's attention to the Visual Learning Bridge at the top of the page. *In this lesson, you will explore patterns that help you see how numbers that are in the same column of a 100s chart are alike.*

2 Guided Practice

Remind children that they are looking for patterns that help them see how to get from a one-digit number to a teen number.

Exercise 1
Error Intervention

If children do not see a connection between 9 and 19,

then ask them how many counters there are in the ten-frame that shows 9 [9] and how many there are in the bottom ten-frame that shows 19 [9]. Point out that the number in each is the same.

Do you understand? *What number patterns can you find on the first two rows of the 100s chart?* [Each number in the second row of the 100s board is ten more than the number on top of it.]

Reteaching Have children show 9 on the lowest of the three ten frames. Then have them place counters on the middle ten-frame so there are 19 counters showing in all. Elicit or explain that going from 9 to 19 requires adding a completed ten frame, or 10.

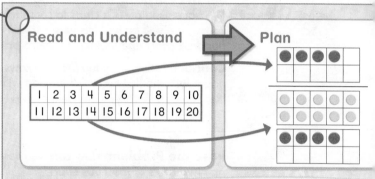

Read and Understand

1	2	3	4	5	6	7	8	9	10
11	12	13	14	15	16	17	18	19	20

Plan

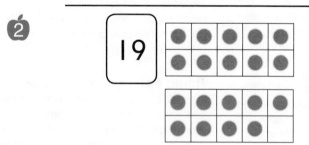

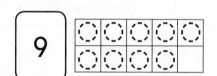

9

19

$10 + 9 = 19$

Directions For the number pair 9 and 19, have children: **1.** fill in the top ten frame to show the number 9; **2.** fill in bottom ten frames to show the number 19 and write the number sentence to match the drawing in the ten frames.

Topic 10 • Lesson 4

Solve

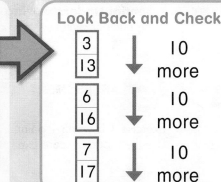

4 ones
1 ten
+
4 ones

$10 + 4 = 14$

What does the yellow box show? [one group of 10; a full ten frame] *What do the red boxes show?* [the 4 ones; the counters in an incomplete ten frame] *What do you have to do to get from 4 to 14?* [Add 10.]

Look Back and Check

3		10
13	↓	more
6		10
16	↓	more
7		10
17	↓	more

This box shows some other number pairs where one number is just above the other. Do these number pairs show the same pattern as 4 and 14? [Yes, the bottom number always is 10 more than the top number.]

Solve

4 ones
1 ten
+
4 ones

$10 + 4 = 14$

Look Back and Check

3		10
13	↓	more
6		10
16	↓	more
7		10
17	↓	more

Additional Activity

Making Numbers

⏱ 10 min 👥

Materials (per pair) 2 ten frames, counters, Number Cards 5–9 (Teaching Tool 5), Number Cards 15–19 (Teaching Tool 6) (there can be multiple cards with each number)

- Divide the class into pairs. Give each pair one card from each set.
- Partners predict whether the numbers they got are 10 apart.
- Partners work together to build both numbers on ten-frames. Note that they will need to use two ten-frames to represent the two-digit number.
- Partners check their prediction. If the numbers are 10 apart, they write the number sentence. Then they trade their cards in for a new pair and do it again as time permits.

3

1	2	3	4	5	6	7	8	9	10
11	12	13	14	15	16	17	18	19	20

4

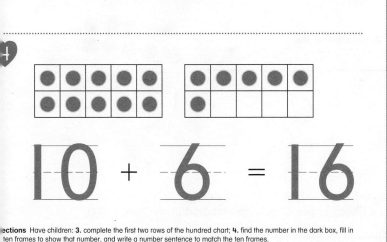

$$10 + 6 = 16$$

Directions Have children: **3.** complete the first two rows of the hundred chart; **4.** find the number in the dark box, fill in ten frames to show that number, and write a number sentence to match the ten frames.

two hundred   200

---

3 **Independent Practice**

Remind children that they can use patterns to help them find the number in the dark box and write the number sentence. Emphasize that they can use the number in the box above the dark box to guide them.

Close

Essential Understanding Patterns on the hundreds chart can be represented using number sentences and drawings.

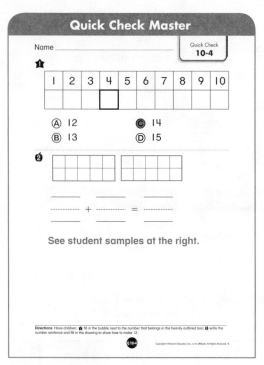

Formative Assessment

Use the **Quick Check** to assess children's understanding.

ASSESSMENT

Exercise 1 is worth 1 point.
Use the rubric to score Exercise 2.

Exercise 2
Make Sense of Problems Children should write the number sentence and fill in the drawing to show how to make 12.

ELL Visualize For children who work best visually, ask them to get a picture in their minds of what 12 looks like on the ten frames before starting to solve the problem.

Student Samples
3-point answer The child writes the number sentence $10 + 2 = 12$ and draws a picture showing 10 counters in the first ten frame and 2 in the second.

2-point answer The child writes the number sentence $10 + 2 = 12$ but does not draw a picture that shows 10 and 2 more.

1-point answer The child does not write the number sentence $10 + 2 = 12$.

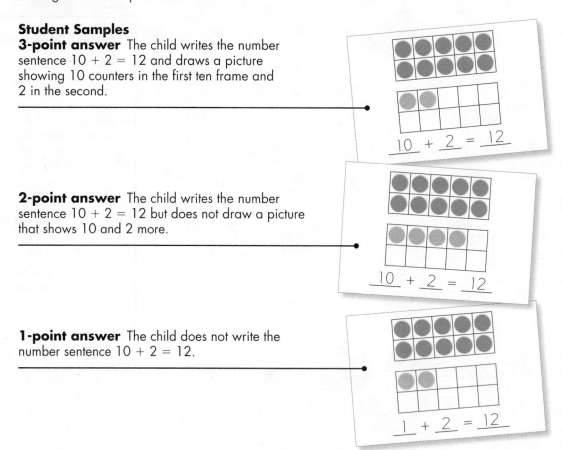

Prescription for Differentiated Instruction
Use children's work on the **Quick Check** to prescribe differentiated instruction.

Points	Prescription
0–2	Intervention
3	On-Level
4	Advanced

Differentiated Instruction

Intervention

Problem Solving: Look for a Pattern

  10–15 min

Materials Top two rows of 100s chart, colored squares

- Have children study the 100s chart closely.
- Cover up the number 14 so it cannot be seen.
- Have children talk to each other about the missing number.
- Draw out that 14 is just below 4, and that each number has the digit 4 on the right. Draw out as well that if you start at 4 and count 10 more, you end at 14.
- Repeat, covering 16, 18, and 11, if needed.

Practice — On-Level — Center Activity

Practice — Advanced — Center Activity

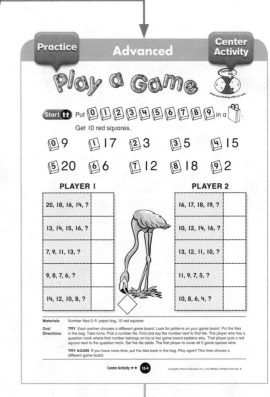

ELL Partner Talk Listen for children to correctly identify the number patterns they see.

Leveled Homework

Reteaching Master

Also available in print

Practice Master

Also available in print

Enrichment Master

Also available in print

DIGITAL eTools **Counters**
www.pearsonsuccessnet.com

DIGITAL eTools **Counters**
www.pearsonsuccessnet.com

DIGITAL eTools **Counters**
www.pearsonsuccessnet.com

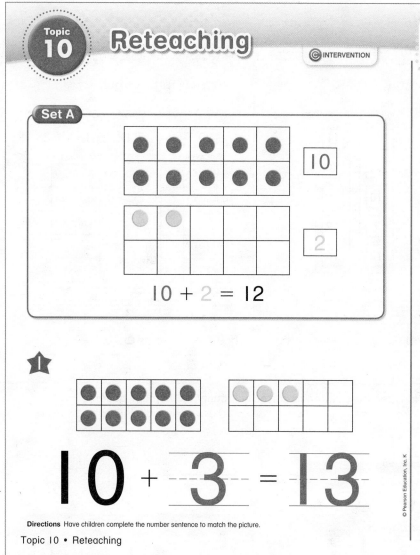

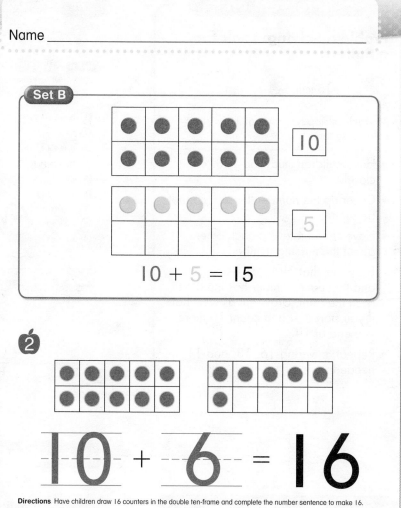

Purpose

- Provide children with more examples and practice for each lesson in the topic.

- For intervention materials, use the resources listed in the chart to the right.

Item Analysis for Diagnosis and Intervention

Objective	© Common Core Standards	Exercises	Student Book Lessons	Intervention System
Identify the numbers 11, 12, and 13 as the sum of a ten and some ones.	K.NBT.1	Set A	10-1	B28
Represent the numbers 14, 15, and 16 on double ten-frames and write a matching number sentence.	K.NBT.1	Set B	10-2	B28
Determine how many more ones must be added to 10 to make a sum of 17, 18, or 19.	K.NBT.1	Set C	10-3	B28
Use patterns to identify numbers that are 10 greater than single-digit numbers.	K.NBT.1	Set D	10-4	A75

Reteaching

INTERVENTION

Set C

10

7

10 + 7 = 17

Set D

| 1 | 2 | 3 | 4 | 5 | 6 | 7 | 8 | 9 | 10 |
| 11 | 12 | 13 | 14 | 15 | 16 | 17 | 18 | 19 | 20 |

13 is 10 more than 3.   10 + 3 = 13

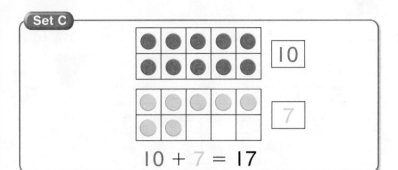

10

9

10 + 9 = 19

| 1 | 2 | 3 | 4 | 5 | 6 | 7 | 8 | 9 | 10 |
| 11 | 12 | 13 | 14 | 15 | 16 | 17 | 18 | 19 | 20 |

15   is 10 more than 5.

10 + 5 = 15

Directions Have children write how many counters are in each ten-frame and complete the number sentence to tell how many more they need to make 19.

Topic 10 • Reteaching

Directions Have children write the correct number in the empty square. Then have children complete the sentence and the number sentence.

© Pearson Education, Inc. K

two hundred two   202

Response to Intervention

RTI TIER 1 ONGOING	**Ongoing Intervention** • Lessons with guiding questions to assess understanding • Support to prevent misconceptions and to reteach
RTI TIER 2 STRATEGIC	**Strategic Intervention** • Targeted to small groups who need more support • Easy to implement
RTI TIER 3 INTENSIVE	**Intensive Intervention** • Instruction to accelerate progress • Instruction focused on foundational skills

Topic 10 **Test** ⓒ ASSESSMENT

Name _____

1. 10 + 2 = 12

Ⓐ 　　　　　 Ⓒ

Ⓑ 　　　　　 Ⓓ

2.

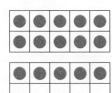

Ⓐ 10 + 6 = 16　　Ⓒ 10 + 5 = 15

Ⓑ 10 + 4 = 14　　Ⓓ 10 + 3 = 13

3.

1	2	3	4	5	6	7	8	9	10
11	12	13	14	15	16	17	18	**19**	20

4.

$$10 + 9 = 19$$

Multiple-Choice Directions Have children mark the best answer. **1.** Which picture matches the number sentence? **2.** Which number sentence tells about the picture?

Topic 10 • Test

Constructed-Response Directions Have children: **3.** complete the rows of the hundred chart and then fill in the ten-frames to show the number in the dark box; **4.** write the number sentence to match the ten frames you filled in for exercise 3.

two hundred three　**203**

Purpose

- Assess children's understanding of the concepts and skills in Topic 10 using multiple-choice and constructed-response formats.

- Additional assessment options can be found in the Teacher Resource Masters.

- For intervention materials that correspond to all tests, use the resources listed in the chart on the next page.

Test-Taking Tips

Discuss with children the following tips for test success.

Understand the Question
- Look for important words.
- Turn the question into a statement: "I need to find out…"

Gather Information
- Get information from text.
- Get information from pictures, maps, diagrams, tables, and graphs.

Make a Plan
- Think about problem-solving skills and strategies.
- Choose computation methods.

Make Smart Choices
- Eliminate wrong answers.
- Try working backward from an answer.
- Check answers for reasonableness; estimate.

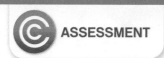

Item Analysis for Diagnosis and Intervention

Objective	© Common Core Standards	Test Items	Student Book Items	Intervention System
Identify a drawing whose parts match those in a number sentence.	K.NBT.1	1	10-1	A-15
Identify a number sentence whose parts match those in a picture.	K.NBT.1	2	10-2	A-15
Fill in a missing number in a hundreds chart and draw a picture to match one of the numbers.	K.NBT.1	3	10-4	A-15
Fill in double 10-frames to represent a number; write a related number sentence.	K.NBT.1	3, 4	10-3	A-15

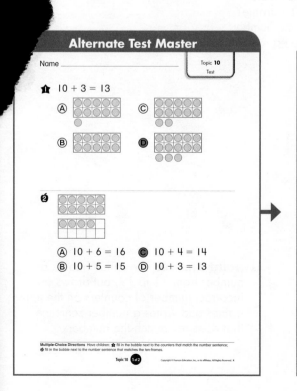

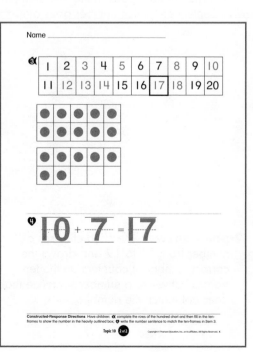

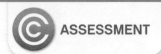

Purpose Assess students' understanding of concepts and skills in Topic 10 through a performance-based task.

Task For this assessment, students choose a number from 11–19 and then represent it by using ten-frames and by using a number sentence.

Get Ready Review how to use ten-frames and how to write number sentences.

Guiding the Activity Stress that children may choose any teen number from 11 to 19. Remind

children that they need to write a number sentence that begins with 10.

Questioning Strategies How many berries did you choose? How many ten frames do you need to represent that number? Will you fill the first ten frame? Will you fill the second ten frame? What number goes in the first blank in the number sentence? Which number goes after the equals sign?

Scoring Rubric

3-point answer The child chooses a number from 11 to 19, draws the correct number of counters on the ten frames, and writes a number sentence that begins with 10 and matches the number.

2-point answer The child chooses a number from 11 to 19 and draws the correct number of counters on the ten frames but writes a number sentence that does not match the number.

1-point answer The child chooses a number from 11 to 19, but draws an incorrect number of counters on the ten-frames and writes a number sentence that does not match the number.